If You're So Smart, Prove It!

Amusing Word Games For All Ages

by Pat Battaglia

International Puzzle Features
www.CleverPuzzles.com

If You're So Smart, Prove It!

Amusing Word Games For All Ages

by Pat Battaglia

ISBN: 978-0-9708253-9-1

Published by
International Puzzle Features
4507 Panther Place, Charlotte, NC 28269
(704) 921-1818
www.CleverPuzzles.com

Printed in the United States of America

Cover design and illustration by J. Pittman

First Edition

First Printing

Also Available
by Pat Battaglia

Are You Smart, or What?
A Bizarre Book of Games & Fun for Everyone

So You Think You're Smart
150 Fun and Challenging Brain Teasers

Thanks to my family, friends and all the wonderful people that the Lord has placed in my path that have given me the help and encouragement to turn my pastime into my profession.

P. B.

Contributors

The following people contributed word games that are included in this book.

Erin Cabatingan, Seaside, CA

Doris Clarke, New York, NY

Darrel Elmore, Ft. Lauderdale, FL

Janet Geandreau, Niagara Falls, NY

John Johnston, Manchester, CT

John Leatherman, Sanford, FL

Amy J. Lee, Denver, CO

Irma Montagna, Niagara Falls, NY

Do you have a clever word game?

Send your favorite word games to:

International Puzzle Features
4507 Panther Place, Charlotte, NC 28269

or e-mail to:
Author@CleverPuzzles.com

Contributors will receive $5
for each puzzle chosen.

Introduction in a Nutshell

In case you are not familiar with my previous books of word games and my squirrelly ways, you'll need some help. So here it is:

P. B.

Each answer is encrypted (to prevent seeing it by accident) but can be easily read when desired.

Most games have multiple parts. The degree of challenge generally increases with succeeding parts.

Good luck!

Get ready.
Get thinking.
Get going.
Have fun!

Home & Away

A man left home, made three left turns and returned home. Waiting for him were two masked men. Who are they?

ANSWER: Look upside-down on the **next page**.

1. fast 2. might 3. flat 4. tip
5. pupil 6. hide 7. kind 8. bound

Synonym Search

Determine a synonym for the capitalized word that will fit into context.

Example: He was strong and had a COMPANY handshake.
Answer: firm

1. The secretary was a very ABSTAIN typist.
2. If you study hard you STRENGTH get 100 on the exam.
3. She was late arriving because her car had a LEVEL.
4. The student accidently broke the TILT of his pencil.
5. All but one EYE were promoted to the third grade.
6. A rhinoceros has CONCEAL that looks like armor.
7. Chocolate is the CONSIDERATE of candy many people prefer.
8. The assailant LEAP the victim with rope.

ANSWER: Look upside-down on the **previous page**.

The masked men are the catcher and the umpire.

Double Play

Use each pair of hints to determine the two-word phrase associated with the game of baseball.

Example: dad, insect **Answer:** pop fly

1. precipitation, postpone
2. middle, weedy area
3. three, drama
4. not off, platform
5. adobe, move fast
6. brief, terminate
7. give up, airborne
8. an animal, enclosure

ANSWER: Look upside-down on the **next page**.

1. idol (idle) 2. whale (wail) 3. grown (groan)
4. missed (mist) 5. wring (ring) 6. cowered (coward)

Makes Cents

Complete each sentence with a word that *sounds like* a word suggested by the clue given in parentheses.

Example: The dog found the body by following a ___ . (penny)
Answer: scent (sounds like "cent")

1. The football hero was the young boy's ___. (lazy)
2. They spotted a ___ off the starboard side. (cry)
3. The adolescent turned 16 and figured he was all ___ up. (moan)
4. She moved out of town and she ___ her friends. (fog)
5. She would often ___ her hands when she was nervous. (bell sound)
6. She yelled at the dog and it ___ under the table. (lacking courage)

ANSWER: Look upside-down on the **previous page**.

1. rain delay 2. center field
3. triple play 4. on deck 5. home run
6. short stop 7. sacrifice fly 8. bull pen

Fun + E

Each pair of clues refers to a pair of words that are spelled the same except that an "e" is added to the end of the second word. Identify the words.

Example: embrace, large **Answer:** hug, huge

1. cap, intense dislike
2. pot, window glass
3. metal container, stick
4. sever, charming
5. be seated, location
6. tack, a tree
7. jump, wish
8. stop, very
9. strategy, flat surface
10. worn cloth, fury

ANSWER: Look upside-down on the **next page**.

The word is "seven". The sentence includes the s's in the spelling of the number seven.

Counting Confusion

What word properly completes the following sentence?

The number of e's in this statement is ___ .

ANSWER: Look upside-down on the **previous page**.

1. hat, hate 2. pan, pane 3. can, cane
4. cut, cute 5. sit, site 6. pin, pine 7. hop, hope
8. quit, quite 9. plan, plane 10. rag, rage

Familiar Frazes

Complete the two words of each well-known phrase. A hint is given in parentheses.

Example: o_ _ r the h_ _ l (past your prime)
Answer: over the hill

1. f_ _ t the b_ _ l (pay the cost)
2. b_ _y the h_ _ _ _ _ t (settle differences)
3. t_ _ n the t_ _ _ _ s (reverse the situation)
4. d_ _ w the l_ _ e (establish the limit)
5. b_ _ e the d_ _ t (to be killed)
6. c_ _ _ k the w_ _ p (exercise dominance)

ANSWER: Look upside-down on the next page.

1. ID (identification) 2. IV (intravenous) 3. PC (personal computer) 4. PI (private investigator) 5. OD (overdose) 6. MO (modus operandi)

An Abbreviated Game

Complete each sentence with a two-letter abbreviation.

Example: He won in the third round by a __.
Answer: KO (knockout)

1. The cashier asked the student for his __.
2. She was on life support that included an __.
3. He's an author and spends hours in front of his __.
4. She hired a __ to trace her missing child.
5. Painkillers are drugs. Be careful not to __ on them.
6. The police used the criminal's __ to track him down.

ANSWER: Look upside-down on the **previous page**.

1. foot the bill 2. bury the hatchet 3. turn the tables
4. draw the line 5. bite the dust 6. crack the whip

Outrageous!

Complete the sentence with four words that *sound like* the one word associated with the illustration.

Without regret the cannibal exclaimed that he was __ __ __ __ .

ANSWER: Look upside-down on the **next page**.

Nine men fanned in nine innings.

Perfection

Add the same consonant 11 times and separate the words to spell a sentence.

I E M E F A E D I I E I I G S

HINT: The title is a hint.

ANSWER: Look upside-down on the **previous page**.

glad he ate her (sounds like "gladiator")

Monkey Business

Determine the saying corresponding to each literal meaning. Each saying has the name of an animal in it.

Example: don't hurry, be patient
Answer: hold your horses

1. expressing danger when there isn't any
2. an unethical lender
3. to run around aimlessly
4. informal group discussions
5. a useless try to create interest
6. to annoy or bug someone

ANSWER: Look upside-down on the **next page**.

It takes twenty 9's to number the 100 rooms: nine 9's from 1 - 89 and eleven 9's from 90 - 100.

Number Nuisance

How many number 9's will be needed to number the 100 doors of a 100 room hotel in sequential order from 1 through 100?

HINT: The answer is not eleven.

ANSWER: Look upside-down on the **previous page**.

1. cry wolf 2. loan shark 3. like a chicken with its head cut off 4. bull sessions or shoot the bull 5. beat a dead horse 6. get one's goat.

Vacant Vowels

Two different vowels are missing from the word circle. Determine them and place one in each blank to spell a common word when moving clockwise around the circle.

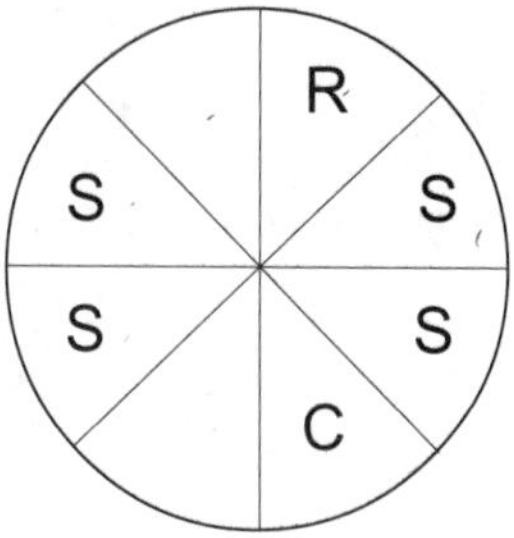

ANSWER: Look upside-down on the **next page**.

1. bee, see, tee 2. boy, toy, joy 3. cot, pot, rot
4. axe, ate, ape 5. sly, spy, shy 6. eat, bat, mat
7. led, let, leg 8. not, nod, now

Three Little Words

Determine 3-three letter words, corresponding to the clues, that differ in their spelling by only a single letter.

Example: paddle, a tree, a grain **Answer:** oar, oak, oat

1. insect, look, golf aid
2. young male, play thing, happy
3. bed, pan, decay
4. hatchet, consumed, monkey
5. crafty, secret agent, timid
6. consume, club, rug
7. guided, allow, appendage
8. denial, concur, currently

ANSWER: Look upside-down on the **previous page**.

The word is "scissors".

In & Out

Complete the two words in each sentence that begin with "in" and "out".

Example: He plugged the toaster in__ the electrical out__ .
Answer: He plugged the toaster into the electrical outlet .

1. She was in__ to a party at the out__ of town.
2. An in__ does not have an out__ personality.
3. Serious in__ are common during prison riot out__ .
4. The highly in__ student received an out__ test score.
5. Lawyers try to in__ jurors to effect the out__ of the trial.
6. Professional athletes often in__ on a contract for out__ salaries.

ANSWER: Look upside-down on the **next page**.

1. neighborhood 2. passionate 3. wheelbarrow 4. forbidden 5. procrastinate 6. hypnotize 7. psychology 8. optimistic 9. orchestrate 10. hereditary

Mix-up

Rearrange the words such that when they are read in succession a single word is pronounced.

Example: rate, sell, ebb **Answer:** celebrate (sell+ebb+rate)

1. bore, nay, hood
2. it, shun, pass
3. owe, bare, we'll
4. bid, four, den
5. ten, crass, ate, pro
6. nut, hip, ties
7. gee, sigh, college
8. tim, tick, opt, mist
9. or, straight, kiss
10. it, red, tarry, her

ANSWER: Look upside-down on the **previous page**.

1. invited, outskirts 2. introvert, outgoing
3. injuries, outbreaks 4. intelligent, outstanding
5. influence, outcome 6. insist, outrageous

Resolution Resolving

John, Joyce Jack & Rachel made New Year's resolutions. From the facts below, determine who made what resolution.

- One person will buy a new car.
- Another person said she will lose weight.
- Jack & Rachel's 8th grade teacher is a blonde.
- One of the four will get a job as an insurance salesman.
- Someone will learn to use a computer.

ANSWER: Look upside-down on the **next page**.

1. be happy 2. can't wait 3. perfection 4. you are a cutie pie 5. lover boy 6. forgotten 7. wise guy 8. too wise to be wed 9. baby blue eyes 10. see you later, gator

License to Fill

Decipher the following license plates.

Example: NICE2CU **Answer:** nice to see you

1. BHAPE
2. KANTW8
3. PRFXSHN
4. URAQTPI
5. LUVRBOY
6. 4GOT10
7. YZGI
8. YY2BWED
9. BAYBBLUII
10. CUL8RG8R

ANSWER: Look upside-down on the **previous page**.

Jack: learn to use a computer. Rachel: lose weight.
Joyce: buy a new car. John: be an insurance salesman

O-kay

What letter placed in the blank and pronounced along with the following word fragment will sound like a familiar word.

Example: __code **Answer:** D (decode)

1. __sick
2. __tra
3. __pril
4. __land
5. __close
6. __pen
7. __cape
8. __der
9. __tist
10. __tle

ANSWER: Look upside-down on the **next page**.

The word is "play".

Up Front

What word can be added to the beginning of each of the following words to form 12 compound words?

back	ground	pen
book	house	room
boy	land	time
clothes	mate	thing

ANSWER: Look upside-down on the **previous page**.

1. C (seasick) 2. X (extra) 3. A (April) 4. I (island)
5. N (enclose) 6. O (open) 7. S (escape)
8. L (elder) 9. R (artist) 10. B (beetle)

Won to 10

Complete each sentence with a word that rhymes with a number.

Example: He couldn't run because he had a __ leg.
Answer: sore (rhymes with four)

1. The teacher did not accept __ homework assignments.
2. She liked her steak cooked well- __.
3. Sometimes a bargain seems too good to be __.
4. He couldn't take notes because he lost his __.
5. A __ field stopped the army from advancing.
6. __ is life's goal for many people.
7. The hostage was released and was finally __.
8. The child was allowed to __ the batter.
9. He had one __ year to go before he could graduate.
10. It was his first __ from that height and he was nervous.

ANSWER: Look upside-down on the **next page**.

Six girls in weird pink bikinis think cliff diving is thrilling.

Bathing Beauties

The same letter is missing 16 times in the string of letters below. Determine the letter, insert it in the appropriate places and separate the words formed to make a sentence.

Sxgrlsnvvdpnkbknsthnkclffdvngsthrllng

ANSWER: Look upside-down on the **previous page**.

1. late (8) 2. done (1) 3. true (2) 4. pen (10)
5. mine (9) 6. heaven (7) 7. free (3)
8. mix (6) 9. more (4) 10. dive (5)

Aging Quickly

What day of the year must it be if the day before yesterday a man was 50 years old and the next year he will be 53 years old?

HINT: It has nothing to do with leap year.

ANSWER: Look upside-down on the **next page**.

1. two wrongs don't make a right 2. beggars can't be choosers 3. in one ear and out the other 4. no pain, no gain 5. pay through the nose 6. no guts, no glory

Huh?

The wording of six well-known sayings has been changed to obscure their recognition. Identify the sayings.

Example: more readily communicated than accomplished
Answer: easier said than done

1. Double errors do not constitute a single correctness.
2. Those who live by obtaining alms are not able to make selections.
3. entering an auditory passageway and exiting from the opposite side
4. physical discomfort avoided yields an absence of positive results
5. discharge a debt passing through the olfactory orifice
6. the absence of entrails, the absence of exalted praise

ANSWER: Look upside-down on the **previous page**.

The day must be January 1. The day before yesterday would be Dec. 30 and the man's birthday is Dec. 31.

Triple Play

Determine three rhyming words associated with each group of clues.

Example: sightless, intellect, good-hearted
Answer: blind, mind, kind

1. male title, skin swelling, a sibling
2. gulp, come next, empty inside
3. spirit, cook in oven, brag
4. combat, correct, after dark
5. tied, raised earth, circular
6. imperial, work, dirt
7. grieve, bugle, a grain
8. trench, connect, throw

ANSWER: Look upside-down on the **next page**.

1. dug (Doug) 2. gale (Gail) 3. fill (Phil) 4. been (Ben) 5. clawed (Claude)

Jim Dandy

Complete each sentence with a word that is pronounced the same as a person's name.

Example: A ___ was used to lift the I-beam.
Answer: derrick (sounds like Derek)

1. The hole he ___ was two feet deep.
2. The ___ force uprooted trees.
3. The dentist was paid to ___ the cavity.
4. He has ___ unemployed for two years.
5. He was ___ by a bear and severely injured.

ANSWER: Look upside-down on the **previous page**.

1. Mr., blister, sister 2. swallow, follow, hollow 3. ghost, roast, boast 4. fight, night, might 5. found, mound, round 6. royal, toil, soil 7. mourn, horn, corn 8. ditch, hitch, pitch

G Whiz

What one letter is pronounced like a word suggested by each clue?

Example: a drink **Answer**: T (tea)

1. an insect
2. a vegetable
3. a body of water
4. yes
5. a question
6. an animal
7. debt
8. a signal

ANSWER: Look upside-down on the **next page**.

Seven. The six candles made from 36 stubs can be burned down to six stubs and then molded into the seventh candle.

Melt Down

Six candle stubs can be molded into one full-sized candle. How many full-sized candles can be made and burned down to a stub from 36 candles?

HINT: Six is an answer, but it's the wrong answer.

ANSWER: Look upside-down on the **previous page**.

1. B (bee) 2. P (pea) 3. C (sea) 4. I (aye)
5. Y (why) 6. U (ewe) 7. O (owe) 8. Q (que)

A Real Cutup

The outside of the cube is painted red. The cube is then cut into smaller cubes as shown. How many of the small cubes are painted on only two sides?

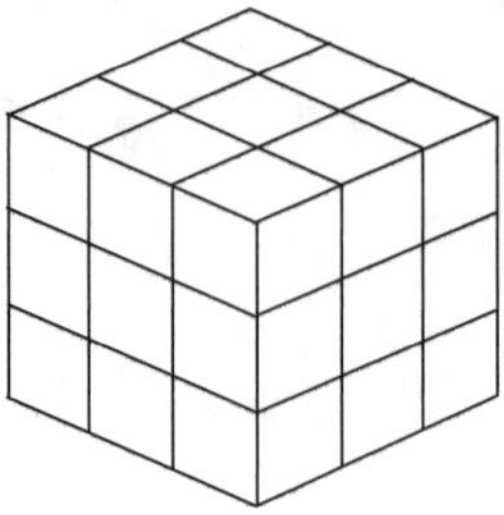

ANSWER: Look upside-down on the **next page**.

1. green with envy 2. once in a blue moon 3. green thumb 4. caught red-handed 5. in the black 6. yellow streak 7. out of the blue 8. red-letter day

Colorful Phrases

Determine the phrase that corresponds with each clue. Each phrase contains a color. (There are five different colors in the answers.)

Example: down in the dumps **Answer**: got the blues

1. jealous
2. very seldom
3. good at growing plants
4. discovered doing something wrong
5. making a profit
6. cowardice
7. originating from nowhere
8. fortunate happening in a 24 hour period

ANSWER: Look upside-down on the **previous page**.

Twelve small cubes are painted on only two sides.

Single Substitute

What one word can be substituted for all eight underlined words?

1. She would eliminate the h's from her pronunciations.
2. The team would have to lose two games to miss the playoffs.
3. She had to lower the hem of her skirt.
4. He was slow and would always fall behind other runners.
5. The parachute jump was successful.
6. In an instant the youngster would vanish from sight.
7. It was a 100 foot descent to the canyon floor.
8. She would often stop by for a brief visit.

ANSWER: Look upside-down on the **next page**.

Dinah soar (sounds like "dinosaur")

Up, Up & Away

Complete the sentence with two words that sound like the one word depicted by the illustration.

Dinah is a skilled glider-airplane pilot.
Boy, you should see __ __ .

ANSWER: Look upside-down on the **previous page**.

The word is "drop".

All Alike

Use the clues to determine each set of three words that are pronounced the same.

Example: we breath it, be incorrect, inheritor
Answer: air, err, heir

1. precipitation, sovereign rule, bridle
2. a country, a spicy stew, cool
3. tear down, elevate, light beams
4. condensation, accomplish, owing
5. penny, aroma, transmitted
6. walkway, a contraction, island
7. two, a fruit, peel
8. to refer to, vision, location

ANSWER: Look upside-down on the **next page**.

1. term in eight (terminate) 2. a bout (about)
3. prints (prince) 4. in tents (intense)

Sounds the Same

Complete each sentence with one or more words that *sound like* one word suggested by the clue.

Example: The taxi driver had a garage with a __ __ __.
Clue: a piece of furniture
Answer: cab in it (sounds like "cabinet")

1. The pregnant woman will complete her __ __ __ months.
   Clue: end
2. She missed work because she had __ __ with the flu.
   Clue: approximately
3. He bought several __ of the original painting.
   Clue: a nobility title
4. The kids like camping because they get to sleep __ __.
   Clue: extreme, concentrated

ANSWER: Look upside-down on the **previous page**.

1. rain, reign, rein 2. Chile, chili, chilly 3. raze, raise, rays 4. dew, do, due 5. cent, scent, sent 6. aisle, I'll, isle 7. pair, pear, pare 8. cite, sight, site

Word Rhymes

Determine the word corresponding to each clue. All six words rhyme.

1. a small collection
2. a sound
3. a premonition
4. chew
5. a sharp blow
6. a meal

ANSWER: Look upside-down on the **next page**.

1. behind the scenes 2. pull no punches 3. bite the bullet 4. scratch the surface 5. neck and neck 6. business as usual 7. out to lunch 8. hang in there 9. rub it in 10. odds and ends

Throw in the Vowels

Insert the missing vowels in the appropriate places and separate the words to spell common three-word phrases.

Example: bckstdrvr **Answer:** back seat driver

1. bhndthscns
2. pllnpnchs
3. btthbllt
4. scrtchthsrfc
5. nckndnck
6. bsnssssl
7. ttlnch
8. hngnthr
9. rbtn
10. ddsndnds

ANSWER: Look upside-down on the **previous page**.

1. bunch 2. crunch 3. hunch
4. munch 5. punch 6. lunch

Back Up Front

Determine ten compound words beginning with "back". The ending portion of each word is associated with each clue.

Example: inflicted with a knife
Answer: backstab ("stab" corresponds to the clue)

1. wolves travel in these
2. done at the 7th inning
3. inflicted with a whip
4. lots of trees
5. dirt
6. causes severe burns
7. often results in paralysis
8. taking it easy
9. where races are performed
10. a political district

ANSWER: Look upside-down on the **next page**.

1. slit 2. live 3. polo 4. trap 5. link
6. door 7. save 8. solo 9. rules 10. speak

This is to That

Complete each word association.

Example: STOP is to POTS as MART is to __
Answer: TRAM (This association is backwards spelling.)

1. GIRD is to GRID as SILT is to __
2. DOME is to MODE as VILE is to __
3. LIPS is to LISP as POOL is to __
4. DRAW is to WARD as PART is to __
5. TOPS is to POST as KILN is to __
6. BALE is to ABLE as ODOR is to __
7. RULE is to LURE as VASE is to __
8. AMID is to MAID as OSLO is to __
9. ROCKS is to CORKS as LURES is to __
10. HOOKS is to SHOOK as PEAKS is to __

ANSWER: Look upside-down on the **previous page**.

1. backpack 2. backstretch 3. backlash 4. backwoods 5. background 6. backfire 7. backstroke 8. backrest 9. backtrack 10. backward

For Pete's Sake

Identify the word associated with each clue that begins with a male name.

Example: Native American Indians used this.
Answer: tomahawk

1. Lumberjacks say this.
2. flakes sometimes seen on shoulders
3. a person in a doctor's waiting room
4. What we do for charities.
5. It's what Aristotle was. Plato, too.
6. We'd all like to hit this.
7. It's a type of nut
8. It travels fast on ice.
9. one of the three gifts
10. It's a long dull task.

ANSWER: Look upside-down on the **next page**.

Fred and Diane. To solve, start with Jim. Since one statement is true, they both must be true. Therefore, Fred's statements are false. The rest is easy.

Detective Story

A teacher found out that a boy and girl kissed in the school gym which is a violation of school policy. Six students were questioned and gave the statements below. All statements are true except those of one student. Determine the guilty couple.

Maureen: Don't ask me. I don't tattle on my friends.
Fred: Maureen and Jim are the guilty ones. Not me.
Jane: Diane did it. She's a big flirt.
Jim: Fred's lying. The truth will eventually be known.
Diane: Looks whose talking, Jane! I saw you and Jack in the gym all alone.
Jack: Get lost Diane! I never kissed Jane at school.

ANSWER: Look upside-down on the **previous page**.

1. timber 2. dandruff 3. patient 4. donate 5. philosopher 6. jackpot 7. almond 8. bobbed 9. frankincense 10. tedious

Symbol Spelling

Using only Roman Numeral symbols, spell a word that is associated with each clue given in parentheses. Roman Numeral symbols are C, D, I, L, M, V, and X.

Example: _ _ _ _ _ (sociable) **Answer:** CIVIL

1. _ _ _ (sick)
2. _ _ _ (container top)
3. _ _ _ (not bright)
4. _ _ _ (combine)
5. _ _ _ _ _ _ (imitate)
6. _ _ _ _ _ _ (municipal)
7. _ _ _ _ _ _ (furious)
8. _ _ _ _ _ _ (bright, colorful)

ANSWER: Look upside-down on the **next page**.

1. Mozart (moats+art) 2. Castro (cast+row)
3. Shakespeare (shake+spear) 4. Nero (knee+row)
5. Pasteur (past+you're) 6. Plato (play+toe)

Prominent People Puzzle

Determine the last names of six people by pronouncing the words suggested by the clues. All people are internationally known.

Example: building for worship + a large mound
Answer: Churchill (church + hill)

1. water around castles + aesthetic works
2. worn on a broken arm + manual boat propulsion
3. to tremble with emotion + a throwing weapon
4. leg joint + things arranged in a line
5. gone by + contraction of you and are
6. have fun + there's one big one on each foot

ANSWER: Look upside-down on the **previous page**.

1. ill 2. lid 3. dim 4. mix
5. mimic 6. civic 7. livid 8. vivid

Rhyming Ends

Determine the word that completes each of the ten sentences such that all ten words rhyme.

1. The girl was frightened when she saw __ .
2. She was willing to pay the __ .
3. The child needed medicine to get rid of __ .
4. The glass was filled with __ .
5. She thought the boy was __ .
6. He ate the bread, but just one __ .
7. Her wedding gown trapped some __ .
8. The boys were found playing with __ .
9. The item was clamped in a __ .
10. The wires were connected by a __ .

ANSWER: Look upside-down on the **next page**.

1. mercury 2. dodge 3. infinity (Infiniti) 4. Lincoln 5. jaguar 6. ford 7. sob (Saab) 8. hummer

Car Trouble

Complete each sentence with a word that is pronounced like the make (not model) of a car.

Example: I can see __ with my telescope.
Answer: Saturn

1. Dentists have often used __ to fill cavities.
2. He could __ questions just like a politician.
3. Numbers go on and on. There is an __ of them.
4. __ is immortalized in stone in South Dakota.
5. While on a safari they saw a __ in the wild.
6. The hiker looked for a __ to cross the stream.
7. She was heartbroken and would __ for hours.
8. He couldn't sing well but he was a great __.

ANSWER: Look upside-down on the **previous page**.

1. mice 2. price 3. lice 4. ice 5. nice
6. slice 7. rice 8. dice 9. vice 10. splice

Number Nuisance

One has 1.
Two has 2.
Three has 3.
1, 2 and 3 of what?

HINT: Four, five, six, nine, ten and zero have 2, too.

ANSWER: Look upside-down on the **next page**.

The word is "cousin" because it doesn't refer to a specific sex.

Oh Brother!

Which word is different from the rest and why?

mother
uncle
brother
father
cousin
sister
aunt

ANSWER: Look upside-down
on the **previous page**.

The words have 1, 2 and 3 consonants.

Word Mates

Fill in each pair of blanks with the same word to form two compound words.

Example: pay__, __dream
Answer: payday, daydream

1. key__, __walk
2. wise__, __pot
3. fear__, __thing
4. cut__, __log
5. over__, __over
6. day__, __table
7. under__, __still
8. main__, __slide
9. house__, __house
10. bank__, __back

ANSWER: Look upside-down on the **next page**.

a-8, b-5, c-9, d-10, e-1,
f-3, g-2, h-6, i-4, j-7

Silly Dilly

Match each word in the left-hand column with the silly definition in the right-hand column. For example, a. pasteurize (sounds like "past your eyes") matches with 8. too far to see.

a. pasteurize	1. a bargain
b. hatchet	2. to take your time
c. appeal	3. a dance for strange people
d. microwaves	4. fear of relatives coming to visit
e. good-bye	5. what a hen does to an egg
f. oddball	6. Italian ants
g. belong	7. a drama teacher
h. romance	8. too far to see
i. kindred	9. covering of a banana
j. stagecoach	10. poor surfing conditions

ANSWER: Look upside-down on the **previous page**.

1. board 2. crack 3. come 4. back 5. take 6. time 7. stand 8. land 9. boat 10. roll

Watch Out!

What characteristic do the following words share?

stubborness	handfull	occurence
mischievious	penitentary	harrassment
superintendant	innoculate	counterfit
deductable	preceed	outragous

ANSWER: Look upside-down on the **next page**.

1. double trouble 2. rug bug 3. chubby hubby 4. loud crowd 5. mean queen 6. late date 7. dandy brandy 8. witch itch 9. dwarf wharf 10. deep sleep

Funny Frazes

Determine the two-word rhyme similar in meaning to each phrase given below.

Example: phony reptile **Answer:** fake snake

1. two problems
2. carpet insect
3. overweight husband
4. boisterous group
5. cruel monarch
6. after hours rendezvous
7. fine liqueur
8. sorceress skin irritation
9. small dock
10. profound unconsciousness

ANSWER: Look upside-down on the **previous page**.

All words are misspelled.

Doctor Recommended

A person takes two pills every half hour. How many pills are taken after four hours?

ANSWER: Look upside-down on the **next page**.

1. knew, new 2. maid, made 3. herd, heard 4. flew, flue 5. need, knead 6. fare, fair 7. weak, week 8. hire, higher

Same Difference

Complete each sentence with two different words that are pronounced the same.

Example: To __ a letter of apology was the __ thing to do.
Answer: write, right

1. He __ if he polished the car it would look like __ .
2. The __ __ the bed for the hotel guest.
3. The stampeding __ could be __ for miles.
4. The bird __ up the __ and out of the house.
5. You __ to __ dough for bread to turn out well.
6. A 50 cent __ was established as a __ price for trolley rides.
7. The sickness made her __ for an entire __ .
8. They didn't __ him because he wanted a __ salary.

ANSWER: Look upside-down on the **previous page**.

Eighteen pills are taken.

Medic + 8

Determine the word that is formed by combining the word suggested by each clue with the pronunciation of the number 8.

Example: prisoner + 8 = ?
Answer: captivate (captive + 8)

1. part of milk + 8 = ?
2. cloth + 8 = ?
3. attach + 8 = ?
4. a state of matter + 8 = ?
5. a European language + 8 = ?
6. reason + 8 = ?

ANSWER: Look upside-down on the **next page**.

The word is "ghost".

Spooky

Place a five-letter word in the spaces such that five three-letters words will be spelled vertically.

A	T	T	A	A
E	E	E	K	E

HINT: A hint has already been given.

ANSWER: Look upside-down on the **previous page**.

1. cremate 2. fabricate 3. fascinate
4. liquidate 5. geminate 6. motivate

Letter Perfect

Use the clues to determine the two words that are spelled with the same letters.

Example: not fresh, slightest **Answer:** stale, least

1. rubbish, perspiration
2. smell, an entrance enclosure
3. inexpensive, a fruit
4. outer wear, a Mexican food
5. very, silent
6. blemish, halt
7. hoofed animal, water's edge
8. stove, wrath
9. huge, noble
10. despicable, wickedness

ANSWER: Look upside-down on the **next page**.

1. medium 2. fast 3. novel 4. soil 5. hose 6. calf 7. long 8. wake 9. bill 10. mole 11. perch 12. toll

Double Trouble

Determine the one word that fits both definitions.

Example: loud noise, used in tennis **Answer**: racket

1. spiritualist, average
2. move quickly, stop eating
3. new & unusual, fiction book
4. earth, get dirty
5. stockings, flexible tube
6. a young cow, part of a leg
7. considerable length, yearn
8. stop sleeping, boat waves
9. invoice, beak
10. a skin blemish, an animal
11. bird resting place, a fish
12. a fee, bell sounds

ANSWER: Look upside-down on the **previous page**.

1. waste, sweat, 2. odor, door 3. cheap, peach 4. coat, taco 5. quite, quiet 6. spot, stop 7. horse, shore 8. range, anger 9. large, regal 10. vile, evil

Inside Out

What is it that you discard the outside and cook the inside, then eat the outside and discard the inside?

HINT: It's something you can sink your teeth into.

ANSWER: Look upside-down
on the **next page**.

1. gulp, plug 2. guns, snug 3. spit, tips 4. pot, top 5. slap, pals 6. step, pets 7. stab, bats 8. rail, liar 9. garb, brag 10. tang, gnat

Back & Forth

Determine the pair of words associated with each pair of clues. One word in each pair is the other one spelled backwards.

Example: brief sleep, used on a stove **Answer:** nap, pan

1. big swallow, a stopper
2. firearms, tight
3. mouth excretion, pointed ends
4. cooking container, child's toy
5. smack, friends
6. foot movement, home animals
7. pierce, cave dwellers
8. roadside barrier, fibber
9. clothing, boast
10. strong taste, insect

ANSWER: Look upside-down on the **previous page**.

an ear of corn

It's Not Fair

Complete the sentence with two words that sound similar to the one word associated with the illustration.

__ __ me intentionally by not telling me the goods that I bought were not brand new.

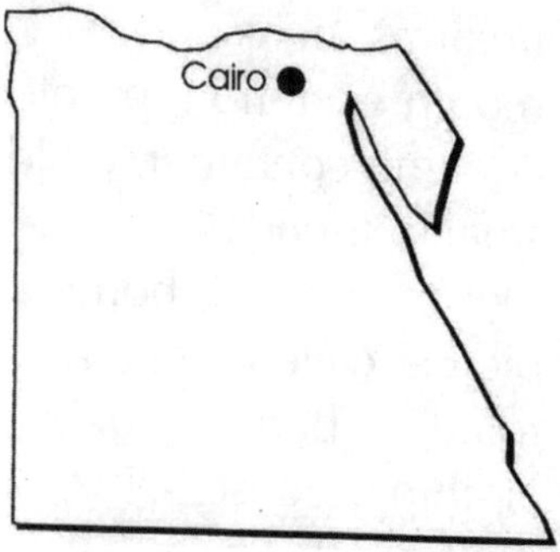

ANSWER: Look upside-down on the **next page**.

All names have a silent "h" in their pronunciation.

Wonder Women

What unusual quality do the following female names have in common?

Chloe	Esther	Sarah
Christine	Hannah	Theresa
Delilah	Mathilda	Wilhelmina
Dinah	Rhoda	Rhonda

HINT: Keep looking. What you're looking for is still there.

ANSWER: Look upside-down on the **previous page**.

He gypped (sounds like "Egypt")

Relate To It

Change one letter in each group to spell four related words.

Example: mob, worm, chord, boil
Answer: job, work, chore, toil

HINT: The first of the four clue words rhymes with the first answer words.

1. yellow, mat, clap, buy
2. crash, latter, dunk, paste
3. steep, dole, cap, pest
4. line, shack, beast, rat
5. guild, mate, product, crease
6. pail, apt, stein, and

ANSWER: Look upside-down on the **next page**.

There are four girls and three boys.

Sibling Stickler

A family has the following characteristics:

- a girl has the same number of brothers as she has sisters.
- a boy has twice as many sisters as he has brothers.

How many brothers and sisters are there in the family?

ANSWER: Look upside-down on the **previous page**.

1. fellow, man, chap, guy 2. trash, litter, junk, waste
3. sleep, doze, nap, rest 4. dine, snack, feast, eat
5. build, make, produce, create 6. tail, aft, stern, end

Suits Me

Complete each sentence with an article of clothing.

Example: The paint didn't cover so another __ was needed.
Answer: coat

1. It's a two-man race and they may __ for first place.
2. When an electrical appliance gets wet it __ out.
3. The Governor decided to __ spending at $1 billion.
4. The lawyer found devious ways to __ the law.
5. The boy's job was __ supermarket shelves.
6. Student concentration often __ off at year's end.
7. A dog __ hard after a long run.
8. The employee always __ the boss upon returning from a company trip.

ANSWER: Look upside-down on the **next page**.

1. monkey bars 2. dog fight 3. bear hug
4. bird brain 5. puppy love 6. crab grass
7. bull horn 8. eagle eye 9. cat walk 10. chicken out

Horsing Around

Determine the two-word phrase suggested by each clue. Each phrase begins with the name of an animal.

Example: type of sweater
Answer: turtle neck

1. playground apparatus
2. war plane combat
3. tight embrace
4. feeble minded
5. infatuation
6. lawn weed
7. loudspeaker
8. sharp sighted
9. overhead passage
10. back down

ANSWER: Look upside-down on the **previous page**.

1. tie 2. shorts 3. cap 4. skirt
5. stocking 6. slacks 7. pants 8. briefs

Rhyme Time

Using the clues, identify two-syllable words with syllables that rhyme.

Example: published recipes **Answer:** cookbook

1. tent
2. knapsack
3. outdoor eating
4. clown name
5. balancing upside-down
6. African tribe
7. wages given
8. performance platform
9. send away
10. incomplete

ANSWER: Look upside-down on the **next page**.

The cities are in alphabetical order according to the country where they are located.

City Crisis

In what order are the cities listed?

Rio de Janeiro
Toronto
Havana
London
Paris
Berlin
Bombay
Rome
Tokyo

ANSWER: Look upside-down on the **previous page**.

1. teepee 2. backpack 3. picnic 4. Bozo 5. handstand
6. Juju 7. payday 8. bandstand 9. dismiss 10. undone

Know Rhymes

All four words in each group rhyme. Determine a fifth word that starts with a different letter and does not rhyme with the other four.

Example: dear, fear, hear, year **Answer:** bear

1. bone, cone, lone, tone
2. hose, nose, pose, rose
3. dash, hash, mash, rash
4. low, mow, row, tow
5. boot, hoot, loot, toot
6. band, hand, land, sand

ANSWER: Look upside-down on the **next page**.

There are twelve F's.

Counter Attack

How many F's are there in the following paragraph?

IMMIGRANTS THAT FIND SUCCESS IN THE UNITED STATES OF AMERICA KNOW THAT THIS COUNTRY TRULY IS THE LAND OF PLENTY. THEY FEEL GRATEFUL FOR THE FREEDOM OF RELIGION AND FREEDOM FROM WANT OF OTHER BASIC NECESSITIES OF LIFE.

ANSWER: Look upside-down on the **previous page**.

1. gone 2. lose 3. wash 4. cow 5. foot 6. wand

Perplexing Pair

Which pair of words is different from the rest and why?

approve, disapprove
appoint, disappoint
appear, disappear
allow, disallow
agree, disagree
advantage, disadvantage
arrange, disarrange

ANSWER: Look upside-down on the **next page**.

1. break your heart 2. with all your heart 3. cross your heart 4. from the bottom of your heart 5. close to your heart 6. to your heart's content

Heart Ache

Determine the expression with the word "heart" in it that is associated with each of the meanings given.

Example: memorize **Answer:** know by heart

1. cause great disappointment
2. earnestness
3. affirm your integrity
4. complete sincerity
5. great concern
6. until satisfied

ANSWER: Look upside-down on the **previous page**.

Unlike all other pairs, appoint and disappoint are not opposites.

Gopher It

Complete each sentence with the name of a creature.

Example: A __ was necessary to lift the two-ton load.
Answer: crane

1. The doctor removed the __ from the patient's skin.
2. The child would often __ his mother until she gave in.
3. He was a terrific pitcher but couldn't __ worth a darn.
4. Some people find it difficult to __ pills.
5. The letter was lost because he didn't __ the envelope.
6. The roof couldn't __ its own weight and it collapsed.
7. She took the advice because she knew he wouldn't __ her wrong.
8. His mother told the teen not to __ down his dinner.

ANSWER: Look upside-down on the **next page**.

Each word ends with the name of a fruit.

A Fruitful Search

What unusual characteristic do the following four words have in common?

appear
sublime
mandate
impeach

HINT: Study hard and you'll find the answer in the end.

ANSWER: Look upside-down on the **previous page**.

1. mole 2. badger 3. bat 4. swallow
5. seal 6. bear 7. otter 8. wolf

Bird-Dog

Determine the name of the bird that rhymes with the word associated with each clue.

Example: speak
Answer: hawk (rhymes with talk)

1. It wags
2. not a consonant
3. fruit squeezings
4. not off
5. bottle stopper
6. ache
7. push
8. royal
9. slender
10. go behind

ANSWER: Look upside-down on the **next page**.

There are sixty-two fence posts.

Posting Problem

A rectangular fence has 22 fence posts on each of the two long sides and 11 posts on each of the two short sides. What is the total number of fence posts?

ANSWER: Look upside-down on the **previous page**.

1. quail (tail) 2. owl (vowel) 3. goose (juice) 4. swan (on) 5. stork (cork) 6. crane (pain) 7. dove (shove) 8. eagle (regal) 9. sparrow (narrow) 10. swallow (follow)

Try Dis One

A clue is given to each of 12 words. When each word is preceded by "dis", 12 new words are formed. Determine the words beginning with "dis".

Example: find the answer **Answer**: dissolve (dis + solve)

1. sudden, strong wind
2. swear
3. a month
4. a women's title
5. recite numbers
6. recreation
7. place something over
8. rushing attack
9. capable
10. small piece of material
11. cottage or cabin
12. without difficulty

ANSWER: Look upside-down on the **next page**.

1. trash 2. dress 3. slick
4. frown 5. truck 6. spasm
7. spend 8. swift 9. clown 10. stuck

Consonant Quest

Complete the spelling of the word corresponding to the clue. The only vowel in the word is given.

Example: _ _ o _ _ a timepiece **Answer:** clock

1. _ _ a _ _ garbage
2. _ _ e _ _ women's wear
3. _ _ i _ _ slippery
4. _ _ o _ _ a color
5. _ _ u _ _ a vehicle
6. _ _ a _ _ twitch
7. _ _ e _ _ pay
8. _ _ i _ _ fast
9. _ _ o _ _ comic
10. _ _ u _ _ adhered

ANSWER: Look upside-down
on the **previous page**.

1. disquiet 2. discuss 3. dismay 4. dismiss
5. discount 6. display 7. discover 8. discharge
9. disable 10. dispatch 11. dislodge 12. disease

Piece Together

Choose word segments from left to right to form 8 nine-letter words. For example, joining the underlined segments form the word "overnight".

dan	ent	ine
sur	erm	ize
<u>ove</u>	oym	ous
som	ger	der
det	eth	<u>ght</u>
enj	ogn	ure
rec	<u>rni</u>	ent
adv	ren	ing

ANSWER: Look upside-down on the **next page**.

1. forgive 2. late 3. tent 4. basics
5. tomb 6. fort 7. tuba 8. wonderful

Enunciate

Determine a word suggested by the clue that has the number, given in parentheses, in its pronunciation.

Example: song (2) **Answer**: tune

1. pardon (4)
2. tardy (8)
3. portable shelter (10)
4. fundamentals (6)
5. grave (2)
6. garrison (4)
7. wind instrument (2)
8. magnificent (1)

ANSWER: Look upside-down on the **previous page**.

dangerous, surrender, overnight, something, determine, enjoyment, recognize, adventure

Safety First

Start at the shaded square and move one square at a time to complete the joke below. Move up, down, right and left, but not diagonally. Use all squares once.

O	D	I	V
N	O	D	I
G	T	Y	N
O	S	K	G

If at first you don't succeed ...

ANSWER: Look upside-down on the **next page**.

The two words are traps and tarps.

In a Spell

What two words are spelled with the same letters?

scrap	smart	tramp	shots
spots	sport	stamp	tarps
start	marsh	snort	stand
carts	traps	darts	sharp
forts	short	spars	snaps

ANSWER: Look upside-down on the **previous page**.

do not go skydiving.

Go Figure

Complete each sentence with a word associated with math.

Example: Rabbits are known to __ quickly.
Answer: multiply

1. A good salesperson will never display a __ attitude.
2. The story was published in the New York __.
3. She was excited to learn that her pregnancy test was __.
4. The speaker was making a good __.
5. The plant will never take __ in such rocky soil.
6. The CEO reported the closing of the firm's domestic __.
7. When applying to college, extracurricular activities are a __.
8. Jane wanted her pay to __ John's.

ANSWER: Look upside-down on the **next page**.

It's an echo.

Riddle Rattle

It has no mouth,
But it can be heard.
It travels in air,
But it's not a bird.

It has no nose,
So it can't smell.
Does that help
To ring a bell?

It's fun for kids,
But it's never seen.
For goodness sake,
What do I mean?

What is it?

ANSWER: Look upside-down on the **previous page**.

1. negative 2. Times 3. positive 4. point 5. root 6. division 7. plus 8. equal

Phil in the Blanks

Complete each sentence with a person's name and a rhyming word.

Example: __ slipped on a __ peel.
Answer: Hannah, banana

1. __ had a __ of stamp collecting.
2. __ works for the postal service and delivers __ .
3. __ is lame and walks with a __.
4. __ sings in a __ .
5. __ loves music and often hums a __.
6. __ is an opera singer and has a powerful __ .
7. __ needed several __ to solve this puzzle.
8. __ called a __ to stop the fighting.
9. __ was a convicted __ with a long criminal record.
10. __ told her children not to __ in church.

ANSWER: Look upside-down on the **next page**.

All spellings begin with the letters of the country where the language is spoken except for Dutch, the language of the Netherlands.

Language Barrier

There is something unusual about the spelling of one of the following languages. Which one and why?

Chinese	Italian	Portuguese
Dutch	Japanese	Russian
French	Norwegian	Spanish
German	Polish	Swedish

ANSWER: Look upside-down on the **previous page**.

1. Bobby, hobby 2. Gail, mail 3. Jane, cane 4. Doris, chorus 5. June, tune 6. Joyce, voice 7. Vince, hints 8. Bruce, truce 9. Ellen, felon 10. Bridget, fidget

Match-up

Match each meaning of a word in Column A with another meaning of the same word in Column B. For example, 1. boxing area (ring) matches with f. finger jewelry.

Column A	Column B
1. boxing area	a. golf club
2. duck sound	b. animal enclosure
3. grooming instrument	c. endure
4. a wild animal	d. fraudulent doctor
5. flexible tube	e. thorough search
6. timepiece	f. finger jewelry
7. used to press clothes	g. stockings
8. writing instrument	h. observe

ANSWER: Look upside-down on the **next page**.

no one listens the first time.

Phony Message

1	2 ABC	3 DEF
4 GHI	5 JKL	6 MNO
7 PQRS	8 TUV	9 WXYZ

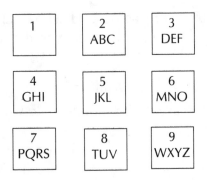

Place the appropriate letter corresponding to each number to complete the following quip.

History repeats itself because ...

_ _   _ _ _   _ _ _ _ _ _ _   _ _ _   _ _ _ _ _   _ _ _ _

6 6   6 6 3   5 4 7 8 3 6 7   8 4 3   3 4 7 7 8   8 4 6 3

ANSWER: Look upside-down on the **previous page**.

1-f (ring), 2-d (quack), 3-e (comb), 4-c (bear), 5-g (hose), 6-h (watch), 7-a (iron), 8-b (pen)

Sounds EZ

Determine the word associated with each clue whose pronunciation begins with the sound of the letter given in parentheses.

Example: grows in water (C)
Answer: seaweed (pronounced "c-weed")

1. start (B)
2. covert (C)
3. exertion (F)
4. mountain hollow (K)
5. arm joint (L)
6. jealousy (N)
7. smell (O)
8. blood vessel (R)
9. get away (S)
10. highest point (Z)

ANSWER: Look upside-down on the **next page**.

Only Jim is telling the truth.

Paralyze

One the following statements is true and the other two are false. Who is telling the truth?

- Jack: I always tell the truth.
- Jim: I always tell the truth.
- John: Jim is lying, but not Jack.

ANSWER: Look upside-down on the **previous page**.

1. begin 2. secret 3. effort 4. cave 5. elbow
6. envy 7. odor 8. artery 9. escape 10. zenith

Double Up

Determine two words associated with the pair of clues that have the same spelling except that one of the words has double letters.

Example: extremely warm, owl sound
Answer: hot, hoot

1. excellent, a meal
2. dry barren region, sweet eats
3. marry, undesirable ground growth
4. sacred, prickly bush
5. approximately a quart, debris
6. a place to eat, what is eaten there
7. after awhile, mentioned second
8. energy, to look slyly

ANSWER: Look upside-down on the **next page**.

more on (sounds like "moron")

Ignorance is Bliss

Complete the sentence with two words that *sound like* the one word depicted by the illustration.

A television anchorman mentioned some news stories and said, "__ __ those stories later in the newscast."

ANSWER: Look upside-down on the **previous page**.

1. super, supper 2. desert, dessert 3. wed, weed 4. holy, holly 5. liter, litter 6. diner, dinner 7. later, latter 8. pep, peep

Digit Dilemma

Place the digits 6, 8 and 9 in the appropriate spaces in Column C to continue the order established in the two previous columns.

Column A	Column B	Column C
1	2	__
4	5	__
3	7	__

HINT: Remember, this is a word game, not a number game.

ANSWER: Look upside-down on the **next page**.

1. eyewitness 2. toenail 3. jawbreaker
4. lipstick 5. gumdrop 6. armor
7. hippie 8. ribbon 9. earnest 10. legend

Bodywork

Insert the name of a three-letter body part into each space to spell a word.

Example: ___drum **Answer:** eardrum

1. ___witness
2. ___nail
3. ___breaker
4. ___stick
5. ___drop
6. ___or
7. ___pie
8. ___bon
9. ___nest
10. ___end

ANSWER: Look upside-down on the **previous page**.

6, 9, 8 The order is the increasing number of letters in the spelling of the numbers.

Two In One

Complete each sentence with two words that *sounds like* one word suggested by the clue given in parentheses.

Example: He used his car's jack to change __ __ . (clothing)
Answer: a tire (sounds like "attire")

1. She looked forward to singing in __ __ . (obtain)
2. They were tired and had to take __ __ . (apprehend)
3. His boat was anchored at __ __ . (come into sight)
4. The practical joker had his victim sit on __ __ . (assault)
5. __ __ from a big boat can cause a canoe to capsize. (become conscious)
6. He wanted a Mercedes but had to settle for __ __ . (have enough money)

ANSWER: Look upside-down on the **next page**.

The coat cost $105 and the hat cost $5.

Costly Crisis

If a coat and hat cost $110 and the coat cost $100 more than the hat, how much does the coat cost?

HINT: $100 is incorrect.

ANSWER: Look upside-down on the **previous page**.

1. a choir (acquire) 2. a rest (arrest) 3. a pier (appear) 4. a tack (attack) 5. a wake (awake) 6. a Ford (afford)

Veggie ID

Determine the name of the vegetable that rhymes with the word associated with each clue.

Example: it makes a buzzing sound
Answer: pea (rhymes with "bee")

1. ripped
2. a talking bird
3. similar to jelly
4. cruel
5. victim of skin disease
6. each person has two of these
7. what you take with you when travelling
8. cleansing action

ANSWER: Look upside-down on the **next page**.

1. top bottom 2. small large 3. floor ceiling 4. male female 5. ahead behind 6. east west 7. drunk sober 8. light dark 9. wide narrow 10. raw cooked

Attracting Opposites

Complete the spellings to get two opposite words.

Example: bi _   li _ _ _ _   **Answer:** big, little

1. to _   bo _ _ _ _
2. sm _ _ _   la _ _ _
3. fl _ _ _   ce _ _ _ _ _ _
4. ma _ _   fe _ _ _ _
5. ah _ _ _   be _ _ _ _
6. ea _ _   we _ _
7. dr _ _ _   so _ _ _
8. li _ _ _   da _ _
9. wi _ _   na _ _ _ _
10. ra _   co _ _ _ _

ANSWER: Look upside-down on the **previous page**.

1. corn (torn) 2. carrot (parrot) 3. yam (jam) 4. bean (mean) 5. pepper (leper) 6. beet (feet) 7. cabbage (baggage) 8. squash (wash)

What's the Difference?

What word is different from the rest and why?

calmed
cheated
commanded
crashed
concealed
crooked
centered
claimed

ANSWER: Look upside-down on the **next page**.

1. down & out 2. lost & found 3. hide & seek 4. give & take 5. trial & error 6. wait & see 7. live & learn 8. show & tell 9. lean & mean 10. law & order

Look & See

Determine the common word pair separated by "&" that corresponds to each pair of clues.

Example: male & spouse **Answer:** man & wife

1. not up & absent
2. missing & located
3. conceal & search
4. offer & receive
5. court action & mistake
6. stay & look
7. exist & gain knowledge
8. performance & inform
9. skinny & nasty
10. rule & arrange

ANSWER: Look upside-down on the **previous page**.

"Crooked" is the only word with the "ed" ending that does not represent a past tense of the root word.

A Family Matter

Mary's dad has three daughters.
One daughter is named April.
Another daughter is named May.
What is the name of the third daughter?

ANSWER: Look upside-down on the **next page**.

1. each word has double letters 2. words are in alphabetical order 3. all words have four letters 4. "e" is the only vowel 5. words have increasing letters

Tricky Traits

Each sentence given below has an unusual characteristic. What are the five different characteristics.

1. Little puzzles usually appear difficult.
2. A broken collarbone doesn't ever feel good.
3. Nine boys went home with toys that they made.
4. When Steven feels depressed he never remembers.
5. I do not like steak served without seasoned mushrooms.

ANSWER: Look upside-down on the **previous page**.

Mary's dad's third daughter is named Mary.

Signing Off

A mute man enters a store to buy a toothbrush. Since he can't talk, he expresses himself by imitating the action of brushing his teeth. The salesperson understands and the man buys a toothbrush.

A blind man enters a store to buy a pair of sunglasses. How can he express himself?

ANSWER: Look upside-down on the **next page**.

This book has been fun.

Finish Line

Change one letter in each word to spell what the author hopes your reaction was to this book.

Thin look his bean run.

ANSWER: Look upside-down on the **previous page**.

He talks and says, "I would like to buy a pair of sunglasses."

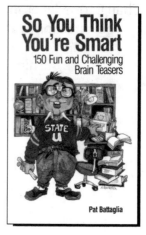

International Puzzle Features
4507 Panther Place, Charlotte, NC 28269

Please send copies of the following books:

______ Number of copies of **Are You Smart, or What?**
______ Number of copies of **So You Think You're Smart**
______ Number of copies of **If You're So Smart, Prove It!**
______ Total number of copies at $9.95 each .... $ ________

Shipping & Handling (total for all books ordered)...... $ 3.45

Sales tax, NC residents only, add $0.75 per book .... $ ________

Total amount of check or money order enclosed ...... $ ________

Name ____

Address ______________________________ Apt.# _____

City ____________________ State _____ Zip ________

E-mail address: __________________________________

Make check or money order payable to International Puzzle Features

International Puzzle Features
4507 Panther Place, Charlotte, NC 28269

Please send copies of the following books:

______ Number of copies of **Are You Smart, or What?**
______ Number of copies of **So You Think You're Smart**
______ Number of copies of **If You're So Smart, Prove It!**
______ Total number of copies at $9.95 each .... $ ________

Shipping & Handling (total for all books ordered)...... $ 3.45

Sales tax, NC residents only, add $0.75 per book .... $ ________

Total amount of check or money order enclosed ...... $ ________

Name ____

Address ______________________________ Apt.# _____

City ____________________ State _____ Zip ________

E-mail address: __________________________________

Make check or money order payable to International Puzzle Features

This is the end of this book,
but Pat will be back
with more clever games.
Keep an eye out.